Will Dan pray?

Fin
on

Have you heard the story of Daniel in the lions' den?
You might have wondered how poor Daniel ended up in
danger of being eaten by lions.

About six hundred years before Jesus lived, something
terrible happened to God's people. The king of Babylon
attacked Jerusalem and captured some of the young men
living there. He took them back to his royal palace to
serve him.

Daniel was one of these young men. He had to work in a
foreign country where people didn't know God. But Daniel
was very good at his job. In fact, he worked harder
than all the other important people in the Babylonian
government. By the time of our story, Daniel was quite old.
Another king, King Darius, was in charge. King Darius
liked Daniel, but this made the important people rather
jealous. Now you try reading to finish the story. We'll call
Daniel 'Dan'. The story can be found in the Bible in Daniel chapter 6.

1

Dan was clever. The king trusted him.

But the king's men were cross. "Dan
will pay for this," they said. "We must
destroy him."

"Oh king," they said. "Give this order. For 30 days we must pray to no man or god but you."

The king agreed. "Pray to your own god and we will throw you to the lions!"

But Dan went to his room to pray,
as he always did. He was next to the
window.

The king's men went to look. "He has ignored the royal command."

What can I do?

The king was in shock. "Dan is my loyal servant."

"Throw him in the den!" shouted the king's men. "May your God rescue you," said the king.

The king went to bed but he didn't sleep.

The next day, he rushed to the den.
"Did your God rescue you?" he shouted.

"Long live the king!" cried Dan. Filled with joy, the king said, "Lift Dan out. And throw the bad men in!"